THE SCREAMING GOAT
COLORING BOOK

© SCREAMING GOAT PRESS & @VALBRAINS 2020

#SCREAMINGGOATCOLORINGBOOK

#SCREAMINGGOATCOLORINGBOOK

#SCREAMINGGOATCOLORINGBOOK

THANK YOU FOR COLORING!

WE APPRECIATE YOUR THOUGHTFUL AND HONEST REVIEWS!

IF YOU WOULD LIKE TO LEAVE A REVIEW:
1.) HEAD TO AMAZON.COM
2.) CLICK "RETURNS & ORDERS" AT THE TOP MENU BAR
3.) LOCATE YOUR BOOK ORDER AND CLICK "WRITE A PRODUCT REVIEW"
4.) INCLUDE PHOTOS & VIDEOS OF THE BOOK IN YOUR REVIEW!

WE LOVE SEEING YOUR FINISHED DRAWINGS!

IF YOU POST YOUR WORK ONLINE, PLEASE USE THE HASHTAG #SCREAMINGGOATCOLORINGBOOK

IF YOU LOVED THIS BOOK, PLEASE SHARE IT WITH A FRIEND!

THANK YOU!

Need a fun gift for someone special?

⇩ Check out our other books! ⇩

Cat Butt Coloring Books:

The Cat Butt Coloring & Activity Book
Cat Butt Christmas
Cat Butt Hanukkah
Cat Butts In Space: The Feline Frontier
Cat Butt Birthday
Cat Butt Halloween
Cat Butts In Love
Cat Butt Or ... ?

more at valbrains.com!

Other Funny Coloring & Gift Books:

The Screaming Goat Coloring Book
The Butthole Coloring Book
The Tanuki Coloring Book
Squirrel Nuts: A Coloring Book
The Tiger King Coloring & Activity Book
Where Is All The Toilet Paper?
Hexes for the Modern Age
Poop: A Coloring Book
Animal Poop: A Coloring Book
It Had To Be Poo: A Valentine's Coloring Book
The Ultimate Bro Coloring Book
Xmas Sharks: A Coloring Book

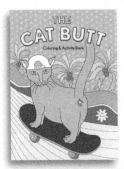

THE CAT BUTT
Coloring & Activity Book

THE SCREAMING GOAT
COLORING BOOK

CAT BUTT CHRISTMAS!
A COLORING BOOK

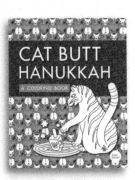

CAT BUTT HANUKKAH
A COLORING BOOK

CAT BUTTS IN SPACE
THE FELINE FRONTIER
A COLORING BOOK

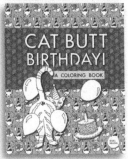

CAT BUTT BIRTHDAY!
A COLORING BOOK

CAT BUTT HALLOWEEN
A COLORING BOOK

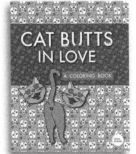

CAT BUTTS IN LOVE
A COLORING BOOK

CAT BUTT OR ... ???
A COLORING BOOK

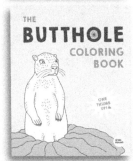

THE BUTTHOLE COLORING BOOK
ONE THUMB UP!

the tanuki coloring book

THE TIGER KING
COLORING & ACTIVITY BOOK
Homage? Parody?
YOU decide!

where is all the TOILET PAPER?
A COLORING BOOK

SQUIRREL NUTS
A COLORING BOOK

XMAS SHARKS!
A COLORING BOOK

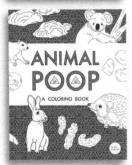

ANIMAL POOP
A COLORING BOOK

IT HAD TO BE POO
A VALENTINE'S COLORING BOOK

THE ULTIMATE BRO
COLORING BOOK

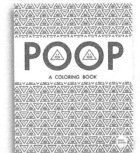

POOP
A COLORING BOOK

more at valbrains.com!

➡

#SCREAMINGGOATCOLORINGBOOK

Made in United States
Orlando, FL
23 November 2024

54324451R00030